My Neighborhood

This mini-workbook belongs to

_____

- - - - - - - - - - - - - - - - - -

_____

your name

Scholastic grants teachers permission to photocopy the reproducible pages for classroom use. No other part of this publication may be reproduced in whole or in part, or stored in a retrieval system, or transmitted in any form or by any means, electronic, mechanical, photocopying, recording, or otherwise, without permission of the publisher. For information regarding permission, write to Scholastic Teaching Solutions, 557 Broadway, New York, NY 10012.

Designed by Cynthia Ng

Photos ©: cover: LightField Studios Inc./Alamy Stock Photo; 6: m.schuppich/Alamy Stock Photo; 7: Mouse in the House/Alamy Stock Photo; 8: monkeybusiness/Getty Images; 17: McIninch/Getty Images; 18: Vladmir Fomin/Dreamstime; 23: Tetra Images/Alamy Stock Photo. 10–13, 15, 21-22, 24: © Getty Images. All other images © Shutterstock.com.

978-1-338-88775-4

Copyright © 2023 by Scholastic Inc.

All rights reserved. Printed in Jiaxing, China.

Contents

Welcome to the mini-workbook for *Let's Find Out Readers: My Neighborhood*! Turn to it every time your child reads a new title. The pages provide engaging draw-and-write prompts related to each of the 20 nonfiction books in this set. (TIP: If your child is too young to write with confidence, he or she can dictate a response to you.) The activities are designed to be easy and fun to do. Completing them will boost your child's literacy, fine-motor, and creative-thinking skills.

Happy learning,
Your friends at Scholastic

Look Up In the Sky

Fill in the blanks. Then, draw a picture to go with your sentence.

There is _____ _____.

a/an   animal or object in sky

In My Classroom

Fill in the blank. Then, draw a picture to go with your sentence.

We have _____.

item in classroom/plural

I See Numbers

Fill in the blanks. Then, draw a picture to go with your sentence.

I see numbers on _____ _____.

a/an   item with numbers

Let's Find Out Readers: My Neighborhood © Scholastic Inc. • page 7

Playground Fun

Fill in the blank. Then, draw a picture to go with your sentence.

This is where kids _____.

playground action

Happy Birthday!

Fill in the blank. Then, draw a picture to go with your sentence.

Get the birthday _____.

party item/plural

We Like to Play

Fill in the blank. Then, draw a picture to go with your sentence.

I like to play _____.

sport or activity

Supermarket Soup

Fill in the blank. Then, draw a picture to go with your sentence.

I help get the _____.

soup item/plural

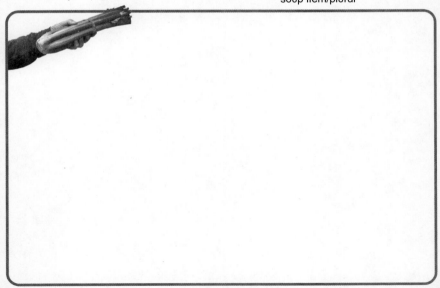

We Walk Dogs

Fill in the blank. Then, draw a picture to go with your sentence.

We walk _____ dogs.

dog attribute

Bubble, Bubble

Fill in the blank. Then, draw a picture to go with your sentence.

Bubble, bubble,

_____ bubbles!

type of bubble

Are We There Yet?

Fill in the blank. Then, draw a picture to go with your sentence.

We _____ in the car.

car-related activity

We Help in the Garden

Fill in the blank. Then, draw a picture to go with your sentence.

I get to _____.

garden-related activity

What Has Wheels?

Fill in the blanks. Then, draw a picture to go with your sentence.

Let's Find Out
Readers
What Has Wheels?
By Pamela Chanko

_____ _____
A/An   color

_____ has wheels.
item with wheels

I Want to Be a Firefighter

Fill in the blank. Then, draw a picture to go with your sentence.

I want to _____.

firefighter-related activity

All Aboard!

Fill in the blanks. Then, draw a picture to go with your sentence.

You can ride on ____ _____.
             a/an   vehicle

A Cold, Cold Day

Fill in the blank. Then, draw a picture to go with your sentence.

It is fun to _____.

fun thing to do on a cold day

What Pet Would You Get?

Fill in the blanks. Then, draw a picture to go with your sentence.

I would get _____ _____
                                  a/an   pet adjective

_____ .
       type of pet

Hello, Helpers

Fill in the blanks. Then, draw a picture to go with your sentences.

There is ____ _____.

      a/an   type of helper

_____ _____.

She/He   what helper does

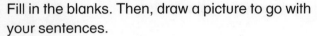

Time for a Check Up

Fill in the blank. Then, draw a picture to go with your sentence.

Let's check your _____.

what doctor checks

City Life, Country Life

Fill in the blanks. Then, draw a picture to go with your sentence.

We can see _____ _____
         a/an   item in city or country

in the _____.
         city/country

At the Fair

Fill in the blank. Then, draw a picture to go with your sentence.

We can _____.

activity at fair

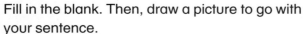